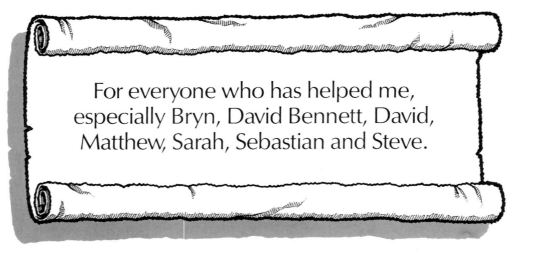

For everyone who has helped me,
especially Bryn, David Bennett, David,
Matthew, Sarah, Sebastian and Steve.

Check list compiled by Stuart Cooper

First published 1989 by
Walker Books Ltd, 87 Vauxhall Walk
London SE11 5HJ

© 1989 Martin Handford

First printed 1989
Printed and bound by L.E.G.O., Vicenza, Italy

British Library Cataloguing in Publication Data
Handford, Martin
Where's Wally? 3: the fantastic journey.
I. Title
741

ISBN 0-7445-1144-5

WALLY'S WILDEST ADVENTURE YET!

WHERE'S WALLY? 3

THE FANTASTIC JOURNEY

MARTIN HANDFORD

WALKER BOOKS
LONDON

THE GOBBLING GLUTTONS

ONCE UPON A TIME (OH FAITHFUL
FOLLOWERS OF WALLY!)
YOUR BOBBLE-HATTED HERO
EMBARKED UPON A FANTASTIC
JOURNEY. FIRST, AMONG A THRONG OF
GOBBLING GLUTTONS, HE MET THE WIZARD
WHITEBEARD, WHO COMMANDED HIM TO FIND
A SCROLL. AND ON THE SCROLL THESE WORDS
WERE WRITTEN:

WHEREVER WALLY GOES,
HIS FOLLOWERS WILL FIND HIM.
SO WHERE'S WALLY?

WHEREVER WALLY GOES,
THE WIZARD WHITEBEARD GOES TOO.
SO WHERE'S THE WIZARD?

WHEREVER WALLY GOES,
HE MUST FIND A SINGLE SCROLL.
SO WHERE'S THE SCROLL?

THEN THE WIZARD WHITEBEARD TOLD WALLY TO
CONTINUE WITH HIS JOURNEY AND NEVER TO
REST UNTIL HE HAD FOUND TWELVE SCROLLS.

FOR THEN HE WOULD UNDERSTAND THE
PURPOSE OF HIS JOURNEY; THEN HE WOULD SEE
THE TRUTH ABOUT HIMSELF.

SO ONWARDS, EVER UPWARDS (OH NOBLE FRIENDS
OF WALLY!). JOIN YOUR HERO ON HIS FANTASTIC
JOURNEY; HELP HIM REACH HIS JOURNEY'S END!

THE BATTLING MONKS

THEN WALLY AND THE WIZARD WHITEBEARD CAME TO THE PLACE WHERE THE INVISIBLE MONKS OF FIRE FOUGHT THE MONKS OF WATER. AND AS WALLY SEARCHED FOR THE SECOND SCROLL, HE SAW THAT MANY WALLIES HAD BEEN THIS WAY BEFORE. AND WHEN HE FOUND THE SCROLL, IT WAS TIME TO CONTINUE WITH HIS JOURNEY.

THE CARPET FLYERS

THEN WALLY AND THE WIZARD WHITEBEARD
CAME TO THE LAND OF THE CARPET FLYERS,
WHERE MANY WALLIES HAD BEEN BEFORE.
AND WALLY SAW THAT THERE WERE MANY
CARPETS IN THE SKY AND MANY RED BIRDS
(HOW MANY, OH BRAINY BIRD AND CARPET WATCHERS?).
AND WHEN WALLY FOUND THE THIRD SCROLL, IT WAS
TIME TO CONTINUE WITH HIS JOURNEY.

THE GREAT BALL-GAME PLAYERS

THEN WALLY AND THE WIZARD WHITEBEARD CAME
TO THE PLAYING FIELD OF THE GREAT BALL-GAME
PLAYERS, WHERE MANY WALLIES HAD BEEN BEFORE.
AND WALLY SAW THAT FOUR TEAMS WERE PLAYING AGAINST
EACH OTHER (BUT WAS ANYONE WINNING? WHAT WAS THE
SCORE? CAN YOU WORK OUT THE RULES?). THEN WALLY FOUND
THE FOURTH SCROLL AND CONTINUED WITH HIS JOURNEY.

THE FEROCIOUS RED DWARVES

THEN WALLY AND THE WIZARD WHITEBEARD CAME AMONG THE FEROCIOUS RED DWARVES, WHERE MANY WALLIES HAD BEEN BEFORE. AND THE DWARVES WERE ATTACKING THE MANY-COLOURED SPEARMEN, CAUSING MIGHTY MAYHEM AND HORRID HAVOC. AND WALLY FOUND THE FIFTH SCROLL, AND CONTINUED WITH HIS JOURNEY.

THE NASTY NASTIES

THEN WALLY AND THE WIZARD WHITEBEARD CAME TO THE CASTLE OF THE NASTY NASTIES, WHERE MANY WALLIES HAD BEEN BEFORE. AND WHEREVER WALLY WALKED, THERE WAS A FEARFUL CLATTERING OF BONES, A FIENDISH CACKLING OF WITCHES, A FOUL SLURPING OF FILTHY FOOD. AND WALLY FOUND THE SIXTH SCROLL AS QUICKLY AS HE COULD AND CONTINUED WITH HIS JOURNEY.

THE FIGHTING FORESTERS

THEN WALLY AND THE WIZARD WHITEBEARD CAME AMONG THE FIGHTING FORESTERS, WHERE MANY WALLIES HAD BEEN BEFORE. AND IN THEIR BATTLE WITH THE EVIL BLACK KNIGHTS, THE FOREST WOMEN WERE AIDED BY THE ANIMALS, BY THE LIVING MUD, EVEN BY THE TREES THEMSELVES. AND WALLY FOUND THE SEVENTH SCROLL AND CONTINUED WITH HIS JOURNEY.

THE DEEP-SEA DIVERS

THEN WALLY AND THE WIZARD WHITEBEARD CAME TO THE WATERY WORLD OF THE DEEP-SEA DIVERS, WHERE MANY WALLIES HAD BEEN BEFORE. AND WALLY SEARCHED FOR THE EIGHTH SCROLL AMONG THE MONSTERS OF THE DEEP, AMONG THE MERMAIDS, FISHERMEN AND FISH. AND WHEN HE FOUND IT, IT WAS TIME TO CONTINUE WITH HIS JOURNEY.

THE KNIGHTS OF THE MAGIC FLAG

THEN WALLY AND THE WIZARD WHITEBEARD CAME TO A PLACE MORE CROWDED THAN ANY WALLY HAD SEEN BEFORE, WHERE TWO ARMIES WITH MANY MAGIC FLAGS WERE LOCKED IN COMBAT. AND WALLY SAW THAT MANY WALLIES HAD BEEN THIS WAY BEFORE; AND WHEN HE FOUND THE NINTH SCROLL, IT WAS TIME TO CONTINUE WITH HIS JOURNEY.

THE UNFRIENDLY GIANTS

THEN WALLY AND THE WIZARD WHITEBEARD CAME
TO THE LAND OF THE UNFRIENDLY GIANTS,
WHERE MANY WALLIES HAD BEEN BEFORE. AND
WALLY SAW THAT THE GIANTS WERE HORRIDLY
HARASSING THE LITTLE PEOPLE. AND WHEN HE FOUND THE
TENTH SCROLL, IT WAS TIME TO CONTINUE WITH HIS JOURNEY.

THE UNDERGROUND HUNTERS

THEN WALLY AND THE WIZARD WHITEBEARD CAME AMONG THE UNDERGROUND HUNTERS, WHERE MANY WALLIES HAD BEEN BEFORE. AND THERE WAS MUCH MENACE IN THIS PLACE, AND A MULTITUDE OF MALEVOLENT MONSTERS. AND WALLY FOUND THE ELEVENTH SCROLL AND CONTINUED WITH HIS JOURNEY.

THE LAND OF WALLIES

THEN WALLY FOUND THE TWELFTH SCROLL AND SAW THE TRUTH ABOUT HIMSELF, THAT HE WAS JUST ONE WALLY AMONG MANY. HE SAW TOO THAT WALLIES OFTEN LOSE THINGS, FOR HE HIMSELF HAD LOST ONE SHOE. AND AS HE LOOKED FOR HIS SHOE, HE DISCOVERED THAT THE WIZARD WHITEBEARD WAS NOT HIS ONLY FELLOW TRAVELLER. THERE WERE NOW ELEVEN OTHERS – ONE FROM EVERY PLACE HE HAD BEEN TO – WHO HAD JOINED HIM ONE BY ONE ALONG THE WAY. SO NOW (OH LOYAL FOLLOWERS OF WALLY!) FIND THE REAL WALLY AND HELP HIM FIND HIS MISSING SHOE. AND THERE, IN THE LAND OF WALLIES, MAY WALLY LIVE HAPPILY EVER AFTER.

THE GREAT WHERE'S WALLY? 3 CHECK LIST
Hundreds more things for Wally followers to look for!

THE GOBBLING GLUTTONS

- A strong waiter and a weak one
- Long-distance smells
- Unequal portions of pie
- A man who has had too much to drink
- People who are going the wrong way
- Very tough dishes
- An upside-down dish
- A very hot dinner
- Knights drinking through straws
- A clever drink-pourer
- Giant sausages
- A custard fight
- An overloaded seat
- Beard-flavoured soup
- Men pulling legs
- A painful spillage
- A poke in the eye
- A man tied up in spaghetti
- A knock-out dish
- A man who has eaten too much
- A tall diner eating a tall dish
- An exploding pie
- A giant sausage breaking in half
- A smell travelling through two people

THE CARPET FLYERS

- Two carpets on collision course
- An overweight flyer
- A pedestrian crossing
- A carpet pin-up
- Three hangers-on
- Flying hitch-hikers
- An unsatisfied customer
- A used carpet salesman
- A topsy-turvy tower
- A spiky crash
- Carpet cops and robbers
- A passing fruit thief
- Upside-down flyers
- A carpet repair shop
- Popular male and female flyers
- A flying tower
- A stair carpet
- Flying highwaymen
- Rich and poor flyers
- A carpet-breakdown rescue service
- Carpets flying on carpet flyers
- A carpet traffic policeman
- A flying carpet without a flyer

THE BATTLING MONKS

- Two fire engines
- Hot-footed monks
- A bridge made of monks
- A cheeky monk
- A diving monk
- A scared statue
- Fire meeting water
- A snaking jet of water
- Chasers being chased
- A smug statue
- A snaking jet of flame
- A five-way wash-out
- A burning bridge
- Seven burning backsides
- Monks worshipping the Flowing Bucket of Water
- Monks shielding themselves from lava
- Thirteen trapped and extremely worried monks
- A monk seeing an oncoming jet of flame
- Monks worshipping the Mighty Erupting Volcano
- A very worried monk confronted by two opponents
- A burning hose
- Monks and lava pouring out of a volcano
- A chain of water
- Two monks accidentally attacking their brothers

THE GREAT BALL-GAME PLAYERS

- A three-way drink
- A row of hand-held banners
- A chase that goes round in circles
- A spectator surrounded by three rival supporters
- Players who can't see where they are going
- Two tall players versus short ones
- Seven awful singers
- A face made of balls
- Players who are digging for victory
- A face about to hit a fist
- A shot that breaks the woodwork
- A mob chasing a player backwards
- A player chasing a mob
- Players pulling each other's hoods
- A flag with a hole in it
- A mob of players all holding balls
- A player heading a ball
- A player tripping over a rock
- A player punching a ball
- A spectator accidentally hitting two others
- A player poking his tongue out at a mob
- A mouth pulled open by a beard
- A backside shot

THE FEROCIOUS RED DWARVES

- A spear-breaking slingshot
- Two punches causing chain reactions
- Fat and thin spears and spearmen
- A spearman being knocked through a flag
- A collar made out of a shield
- A prison made of spears
- Tangled spears
- A devious disarmer
- Dwarves disguised as spearmen
- A stick-up machine
- A spearman trapped by his battle dress
- A sneaky spear-bender
- An axe-head causing headaches
- A dwarf who is on the wrong side
- Cheeky target practice
- Opponents charging through each other
- A spearman running away from a spear
- A slingshot causing a chain reaction
- A sword cutting through a shield
- A spear hitting a spearman's shield
- A dwarf hiding up a spear
- Spearmen who have jumped out of their clothes
- A spear knocking off a dwarf's helmet

THE NASTY NASTIES

- A vampire who is scared of ghosts
- Two vampire bears
- Vampires drinking through straws
- Gargoyle lovers
- An upside-down torture
- A baseball bat
- Three wolfmen
- A mummy who is coming undone
- A vampire mirror test
- A frightened skeleton
- Dog, cat and mouse doorways
- Courting cats
- A ghoulish game of skittles
- A gargoyle being poked in the eye
- An upside-down gargoyle
- Ghoulish flight controllers
- Three witches flying backwards
- A witch losing her broomstick
- A broomstick flying a witch
- A ticklish torture
- A vampire about to get the chop
- A ghost train
- A vampire who doesn't fit his coffin
- A three-eyed, hooded torturer